EASIEST
KEYBOARD
COLLECTION

Celine Dion

WISE PUBLICATIONS
London/New York/Paris/Sydney/Copenhagen/Madrid

Exclusive Distributors:

Music Sales Limited
8/9 Frith Street,
London W1V 5TZ, England.

Music Sales Pty Limited
120 Rothschild Avenue,
Rosebery, NSW 2018,
Australia.

Order No. AM959850
ISBN 0-7119-7793-3
This book © Copyright 1999 by Wise Publications

Cover design by Chloë Alexander
Compiled by Peter Evans
Music arranged by Roger Day
Music processed by Paul Ewers Music Design

Printed in the United Kingdom by
Caligraving Limited, Thetford, Norfolk.

Cover photograph courtesy of Retna

Your Guarantee of Quality
As publishers, we strive to produce every book to the highest
commercial standards.
The music has been freshly engraved and the book has been carefully
designed to minimise awkward page turns and to make playing from
it a real pleasure.
Particular care has been given to specifying acid-free, neutral-sized
paper made from pulps which have not been elemental chlorine
bleached. This pulp is from farmed sustainable forests and was
produced with special regard for the environment.
Throughout, the printing and binding have been planned to ensure
a sturdy, attractive publication which should give years of enjoyment.
If your copy fails to meet our high standards, please inform us and
we will gladly replace it.

Music Sales' complete catalogue describes thousands of titles and is
available in full colour sections by subject, direct from Music Sales
Limited. Please state your areas of interest and send a cheque/postal
order for £1.50 for postage to: Music Sales Limited, Newmarket Road,
Bury St. Edmunds, Suffolk IP33 3YB.

www.musicsales.co.uk

Contents

ALL BY MYSELF

Words & Music by Eric Carmen

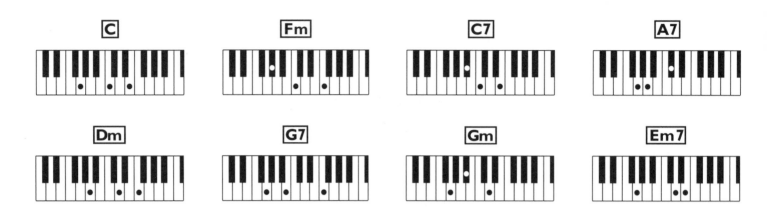

Voice: **French Horn I**
Rhythm: **Epic Ballad**
Tempo: ♩ = 58

When I was young I nev-er

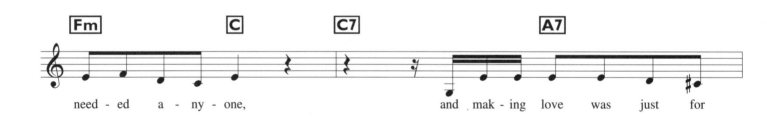

need-ed a-ny-one, and mak-ing love was just for

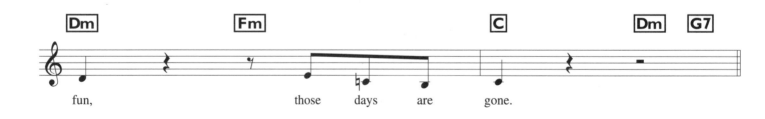

fun, those days are gone.

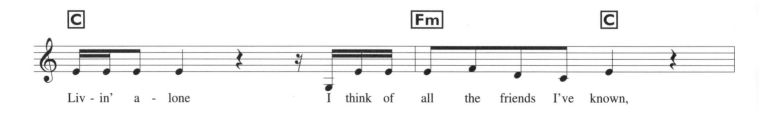

Liv-in' a-lone I think of all the friends I've known,

CALL THE MAN

Words & Music by Andy Hill & Peter Sinfield

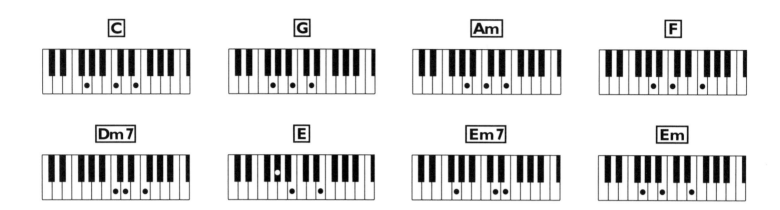

Voice: **Bass/Piano Split**

Rhythm: **Pop Ballad**

Tempo: ♩ = 63

Close the door,_____ shut the world a-way, all the fight's gone from this

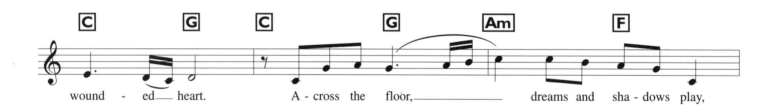

wound - ed__ heart. A - cross the floor,_____ dreams and sha - dows play,

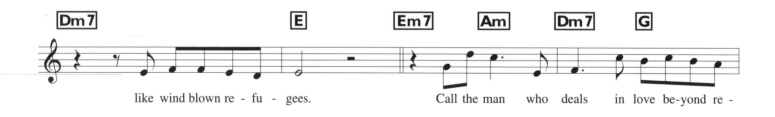

like wind blown re - fu - gees. Call the man who deals in love be-yond re -

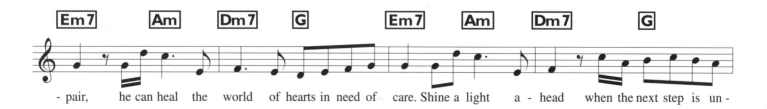

- pair, he can heal the world of hearts in need of care. Shine a light a - head when the next step is un-

DREAMIN' OF YOU

Words & Music by Aldo Nova & Peter Barbeau

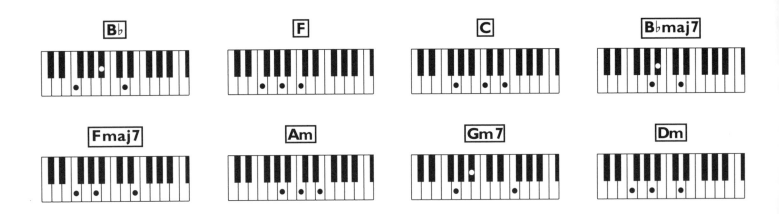

Voice: **Flute**

Rhythm: **Lite Pop**

Tempo: ♩ = 84

Do, do, do, do, do, do, do, do.

do, do, do, do. Do, do, do, do, do, do, do, do.

Ly-in' in my bed, thoughts in my head,

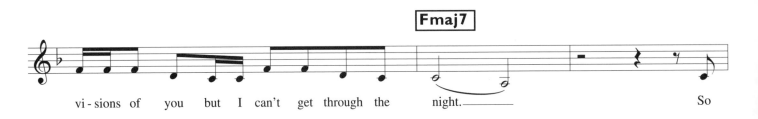

vi-sions of you but I can't get through the night. So

pick up the phone, I know you're home, you're play-in' with my heart and you know that it just ain't

right._____ It's just a game of love, love,_____ love._____

_____ And ev-en though it's hard, ba-by, I can ne-ver give you up. You're the

one I'm dream-in' of, I can't live with-out your love to-night._____

_____ And it's you that I a-dore, you're the one that I live for, in-side_____

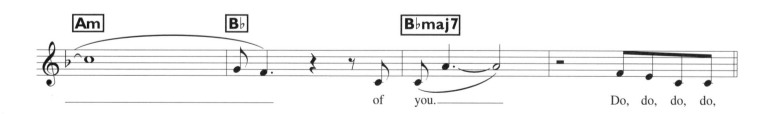

_____ of you._____ Do, do, do, do,

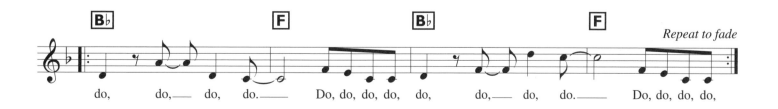

Repeat to fade

do, do,___ do, do. Do, do, do, do, do, do,___ do, do.___ Do, do, do, do,

FALLING INTO YOU

Words & Music by Rick Nowels, Marie-Claire D'Ubaldo & Billy Steinberg

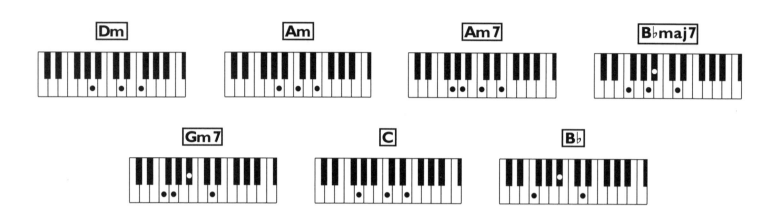

Voice: **Clarinet**

Rhythm: **Pop Ballad**

Tempo: ♩ = 104

And in your eyes I see rib-bons of col-our.

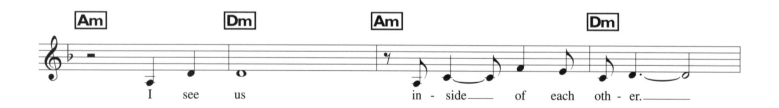

I see us in-side of each oth-er.

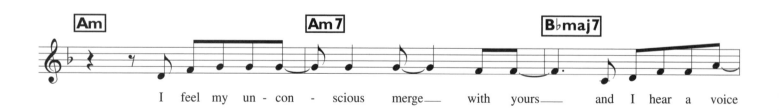

I feel my un-con-scious merge with yours and I hear a voice

say, "What's his is hers." I'm fall-ing in-to

you.　　　This dream could— come true,———— and it feels—

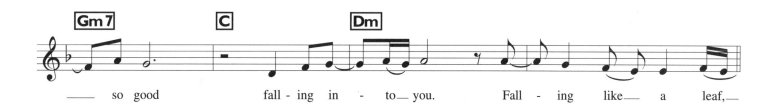

—— so good　　falling in - to— you.　Fall - ing like— a leaf,—

——　　　fall - ing like— a star,———

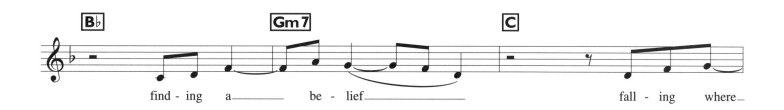

find - ing a—— be - lief——————　　fall - ing where—

—— you are.——————————　　　　　　Fall -

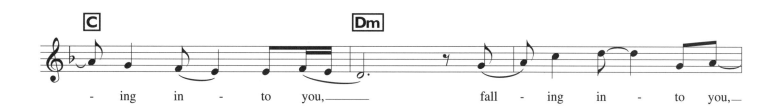

- ing in - to you,———　　fall - ing in - to you,—

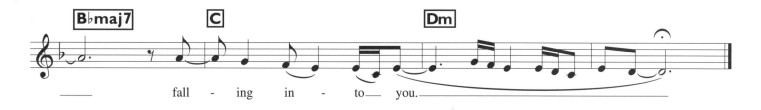

——　fall - ing in - to— you.——

I DON'T KNOW

Words by Jean Goldman & Philip Galdston
Music by J. Kapler

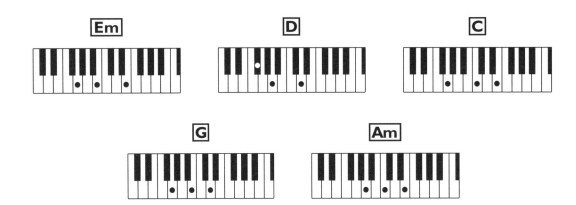

Voice: **Voice Ooh**

Rhythm: **Love Ballad**

Tempo: ♩. = **60**

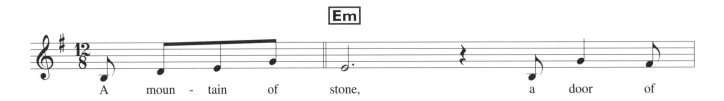

A moun - tain of stone, a door of

steel. Can't stand in my way, I'd go on.＿ Bru - tal mach -

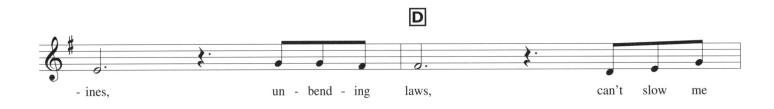

- ines, un - bend - ing laws, can't slow me

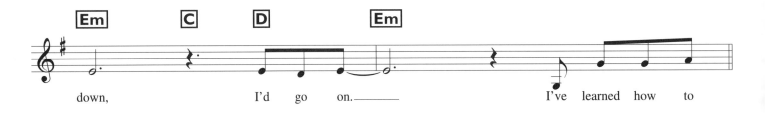

down, I'd go on.＿ I've learned how to

I LOVE YOU

Words & Music by Aldo Nova
© Copyright 1996 Editions Bloc Notes Incorporated (50%)/
BMG Music Publishing Limited, Bedford House, 69-79 Fulham High Street, London SW6 (50%).
All Rights Reserved. International Copyright Secured.

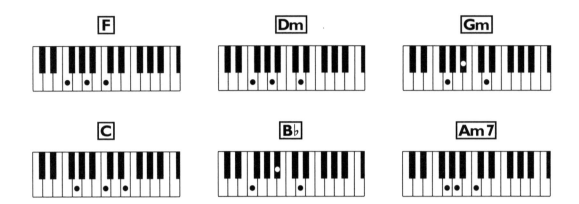

Voice: **Studio Piano**

Rhythm: **Love Ballad**

Tempo: ♩. = 60

Do, do, do, do, do.____   Do, do, do, do, do.____

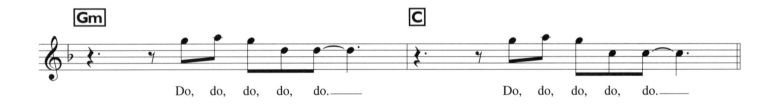

Do, do, do, do, do.____   Do, do, do, do, do.____

I must be cra-zy now,____ may-be I dream too much,____ but when I think of you,____ I

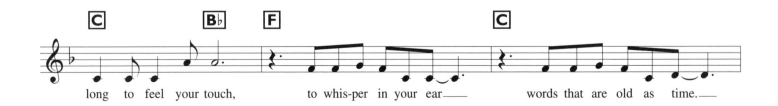

long to feel your touch,   to whis-per in your ear____ words that are old as time.____

words on - ly you would hear,— if on - ly you were mine. I wish I could go back to the ve - ry first day, I

saw you, should have made my move when you looked— in my eyes.— 'Cause by

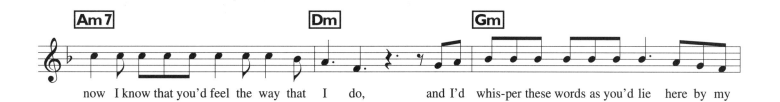

now I know that you'd feel the way that I do, and I'd whis - per these words as you'd lie here by my

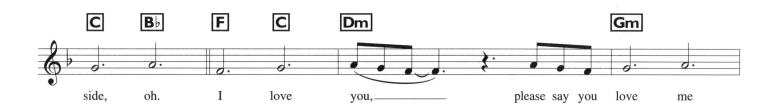

side, oh. I love you,——— please say you love me

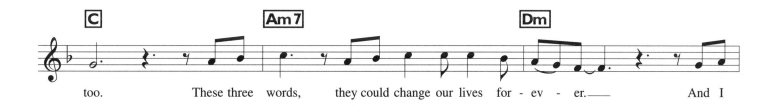

too. These three words, they could change our lives for - ev - er.— And I

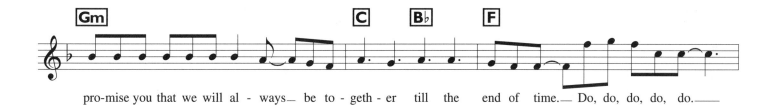

pro - mise you that we will al - ways— be to - geth - er till the end of time.— Do, do, do, do, do.——

Do, do, do, do, do.— Do, do, do, do, do.

I REMEMBER L.A.

Words & Music by Tony Colton & Richard Wold

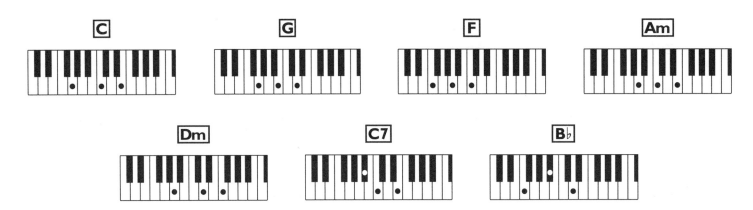

Voice: **Acoustic Guitar**

Rhythm: **Folky Pop**

Tempo: ♩ = 100

I re - mem - ber L.A.,

seems a life - time a - go.

We were stars on Sun - set Bou - le - vard,

what a mo - vie we made.

I'M YOUR ANGEL

Words & Music by R. Kelly

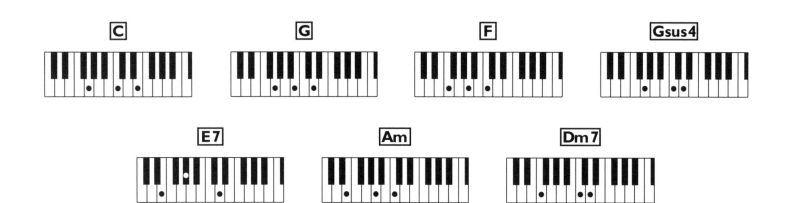

Voice: **Gut Guitar**

Rhythm: **Soul Ballad**

Tempo: ♩ = 108

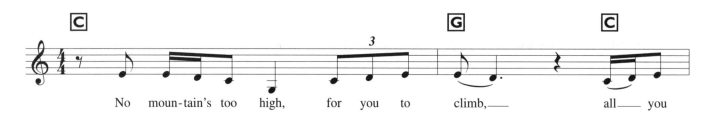

No moun-tain's too high, for you to climb,—— all—— you

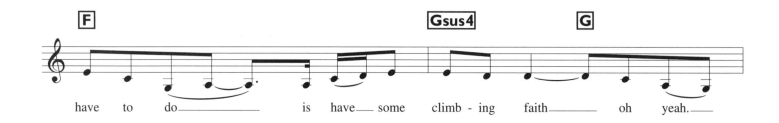

have to do—— is have—— some climb-ing faith—— oh yeah.——

No riv-er's too wide—— for you to make it a-cross, all—— you

have to do—— is—— be-lieve it when you pray. And

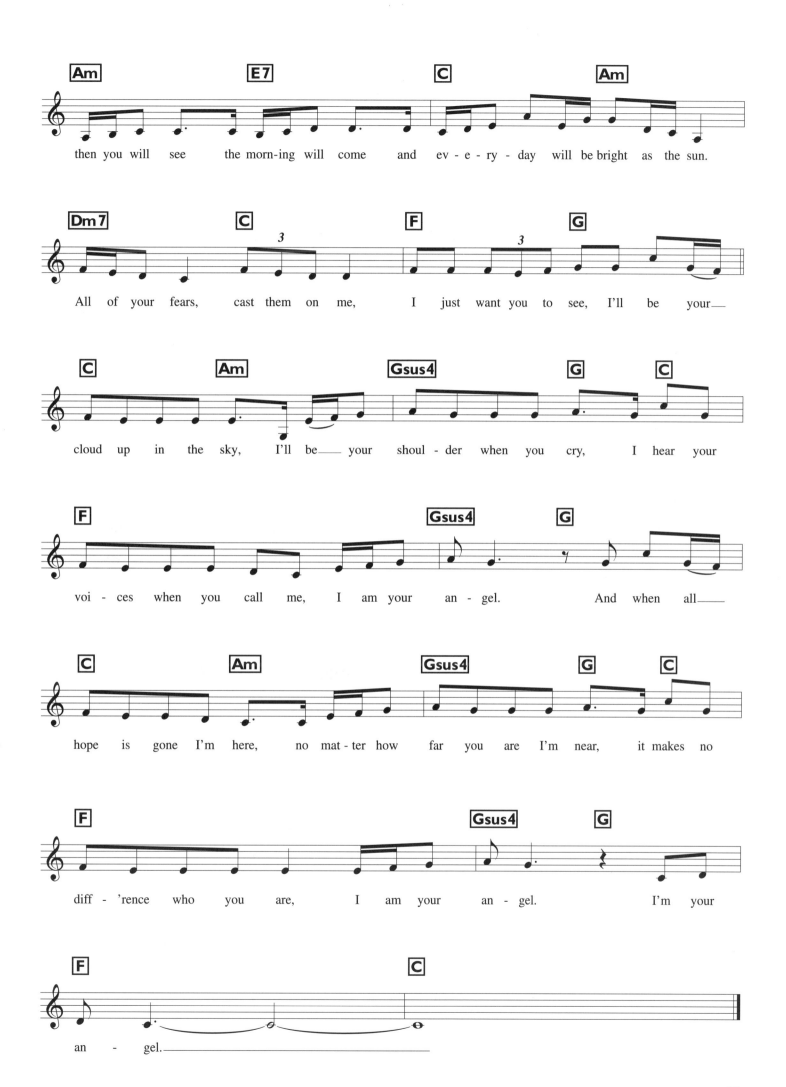

IF THAT'S WHAT IT TAKES

Words & Music by Jean Goldman & Philip Galdston

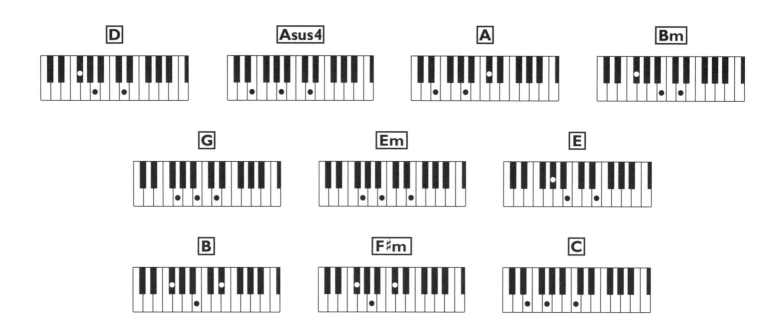

Voice: **Tenor Saxophone**

Rhythm: **Soft Rock 1**

Tempo: ♩ = 88

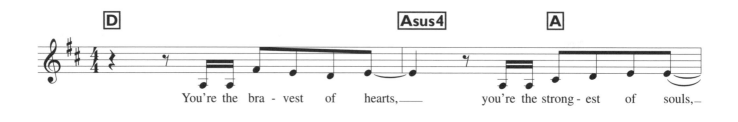

You're the bra-vest of hearts,⸺ you're the strong-est of souls,⸺

⸺ you're my light in the dark,

⸺ you're the place I call home.

IMMORTALITY

Words & Music by Barry Gibb, Robin Gibb & Maurice Gibb

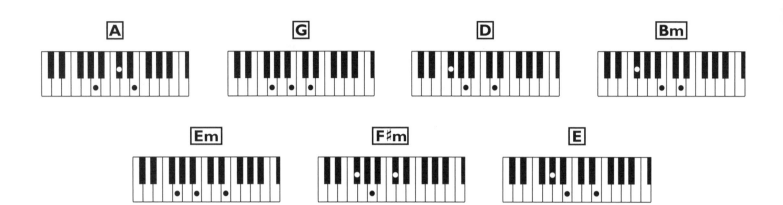

Voice: **Electric Piano 2**

Rhythm: **Twist**

Tempo: ♩ = 140

So this is who I am and this is all I

know, and I must choose to live for all that I can

give,— the spark that makes the pow-er grow. And I will stand for my dream if I can,

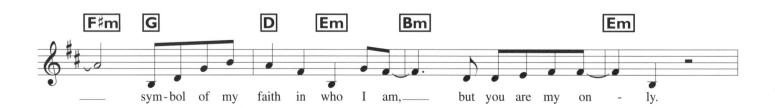

—— sym-bol of my faith in who I am,—— but you are my on - ly.

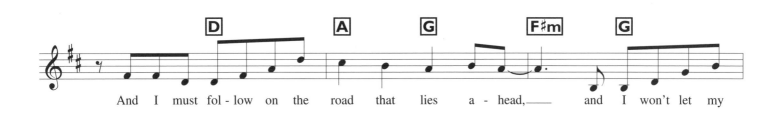

And I must fol-low on the road that lies a-head,—— and I won't let my

heart con-trol my head,—— but you are my on - ly.

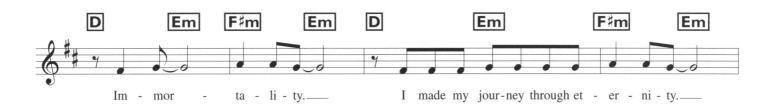

Im - mor - ta - li - ty.—— I made my jour-ney through et - er - ni - ty.——

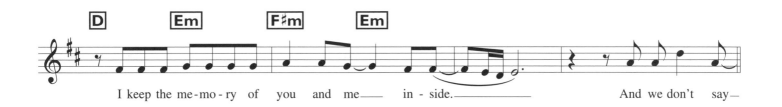

I keep the me-mo-ry of you and me—— in - side.—— And we don't say—

—— good-bye, we don't say good - bye, with all my love for

you, and what else we may do. We don't say good - bye.——

IT'S ALL COMING BACK TO ME NOW

Words & Music by Jim Steinman

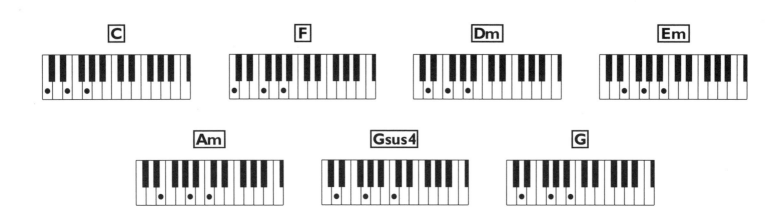

Voice: **12 String Guitar**

Rhythm: **Pop Ballad**

Tempo: ♩ = 92

There were nights when the wind—— was so cold,———— that my

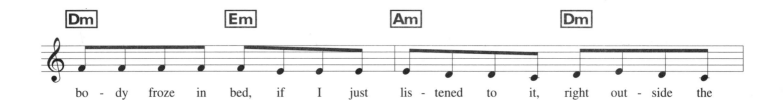

bo - dy froze in bed, if I just lis - tened to it, right out - side the

win - dow. There were days when the sun—— was so

cruel,———— that all the tears turned to dust—— and I just

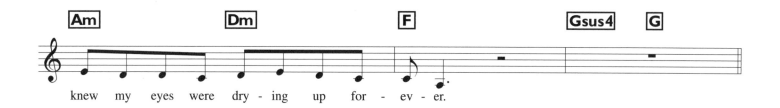

knew my eyes were dry-ing up for - ev - er.

I fin-ished cry-ing in the in-stant that you left, and I can't re-mem-ber where or when or

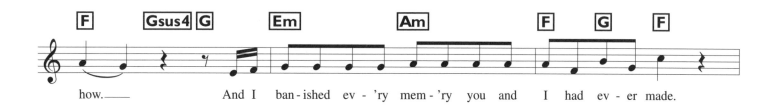

how.___ And I ban-ished ev-'ry mem-'ry you and I had ev - er made.

But when you touch me like this___ and you hold me like that,___ I just

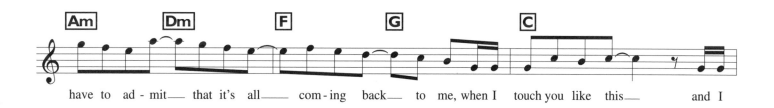

have to ad-mit___ that it's all___ com-ing back___ to me, when I touch you like this___ and I

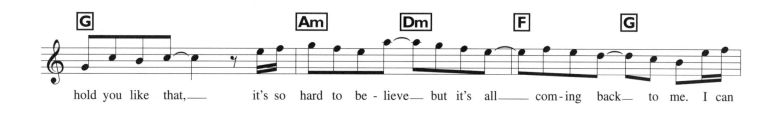

hold you like that,___ it's so hard to be-lieve___ but it's all___ com-ing back___ to me. I can

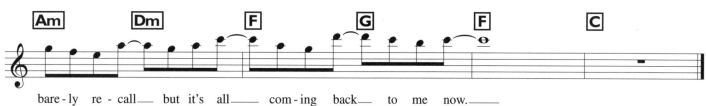

bare-ly re-call___ but it's all___ com-ing back___ to me now.___

JUST WALK AWAY

Words & Music by Albert Hammond & Marti Sharron
© Copyright 1993 Albert Hammond Enterprises Incorporated & Spinning Platinum Music, USA.
Windswept Pacific Music Limited, Hope House, 40 St. Peter's Road, London W6 (50%)/
Famous Music Corporation, USA (50%).
All Rights Reserved. International Copyright Secured.

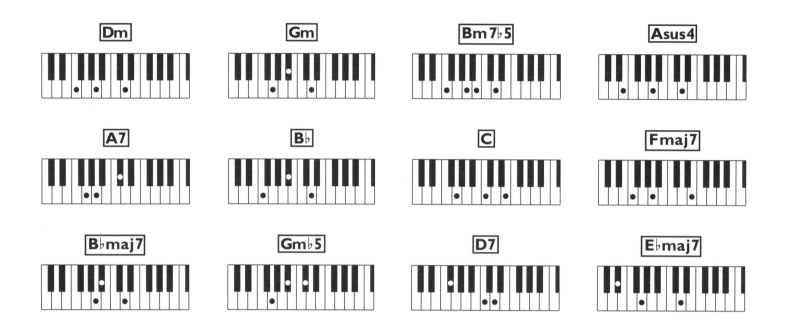

Voice: **Acoustic Guitar**

Rhythm: **Soul Ballad**

Tempo: ♩ = 76

I know I nev-er loved this way be - fore, and no-one else has loved me more. With

you I've laughed and cried. I have lived and died, what I would-n't do just to be with you. I

know I must for - get you to go on, I can't hold back my tears too

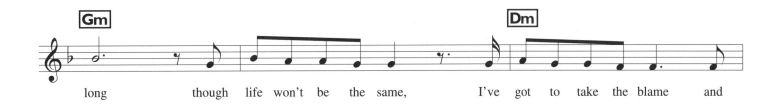

long   though   life   won't   be   the   same,   I've   got   to   take   the   blame   and

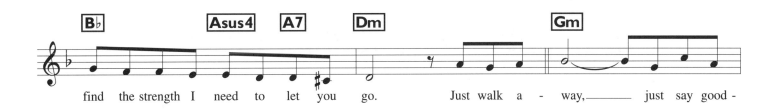

find   the   strength   I   need   to   let   you   go.   Just   walk   a - way,_____   just   say   good -

- bye,   don't   turn   a - round   now,   you   may   see   me   cry,   I

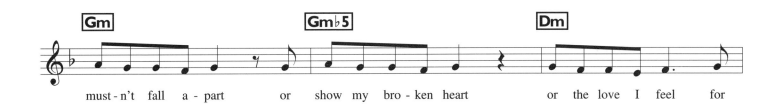

must - n't   fall   a - part   or   show   my   bro - ken   heart   or   the   love   I   feel   for

you.   So   walk   a - way_____   and   close   the   door,   and   let   my

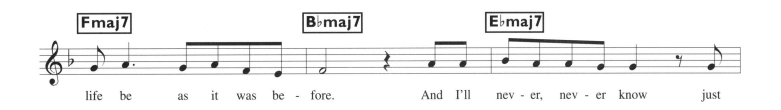

life   be   as   it   was   be - fore.   And   I'll   nev - er,   nev - er   know   just

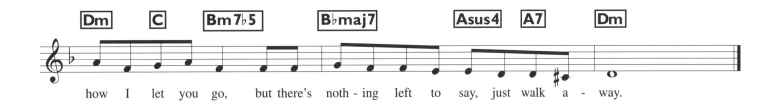

how   I   let   you   go,   but   there's   noth - ing   left   to   say,   just   walk   a - way.

LET'S TALK ABOUT LOVE

Words & Music by Bryan Adams, Eliot Kennedy & Jean-Jacques Goldman

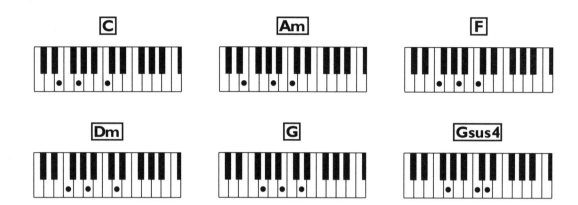

Voice: **Piano 1**

Rhythm: **Soul Ballad**

Tempo: ♩ = 68

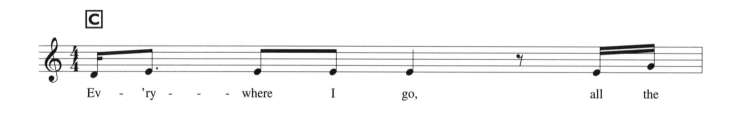

Ev-'ry-where I go, all the

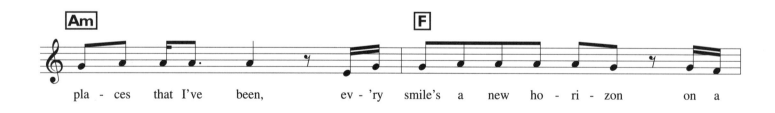

pla-ces that I've been, ev-'ry smile's a new ho-ri-zon on a

land I've nev-er seen. There are peo-ple a-round the world, diff-'rent

Repeat to fade

LOVE DOESN'T ASK WHY

Words & Music by Philip Galdston, Barry Mann & Cynthia Weil

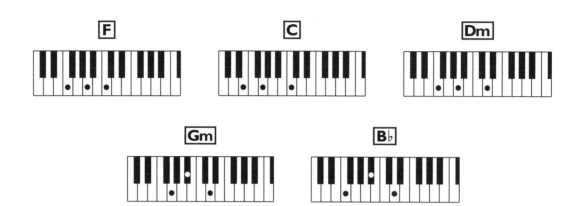

Voice: **Choir**

Rhythm: **Pop Rock 1**

Tempo: ♩ = 76

Love does-n't ask why, it speaks from the heart,

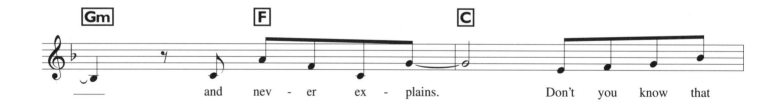

and nev-er ex-plains. Don't you know that

love does-n't think twice, it can all come at once

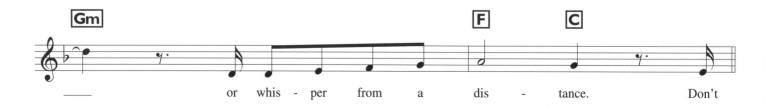

or whis-per from a dis-tance. Don't

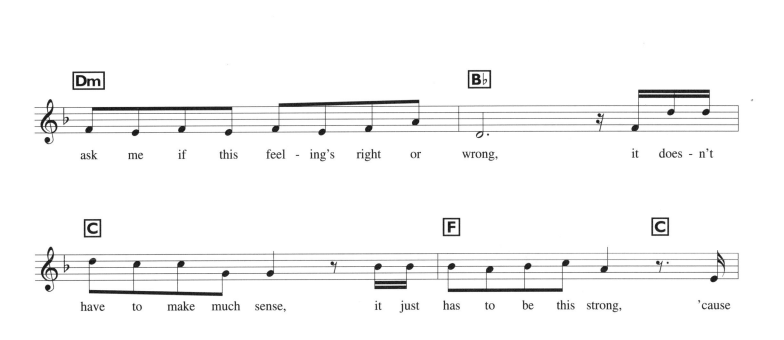

ask me if this feel-ing's right or wrong, it does-n't

have to make much sense, it just has to be this strong, 'cause

when you're in my arms I un-der-stand, we don't have a voice___ when our

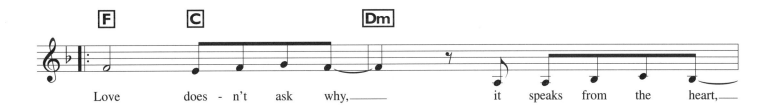

hearts make the choi - ces, there's no plan, it... it's not in our hands.

Love does - n't ask why,___ it speaks from the heart,___

Repeat to fade

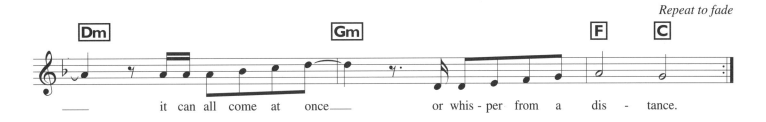

___ and nev - er ex - plains.___ Don't you know that love does - n't think twice,___

___ it can all come at once___ or whis - per from a dis - tance.

MY HEART WILL GO ON

Words and Music by Will Jennings and James Horner

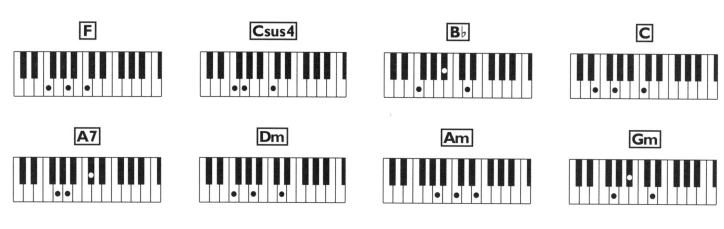

Voice: **Electric Piano 1**

Rhythm: **Pop Ballad**

Tempo: ♩ = 128

Ev - 'ry night in my dreams, I see you, I

feel_____ you. That is how I know you go

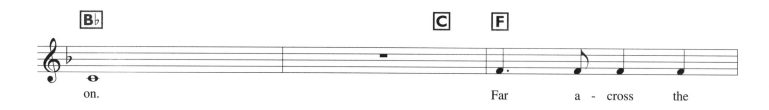

on. Far a - cross the

dis - tance and spa - ces be - tween_____ us,

SEDUCES ME

Words by Dan Hill
Music by Dan Hill & John Shead

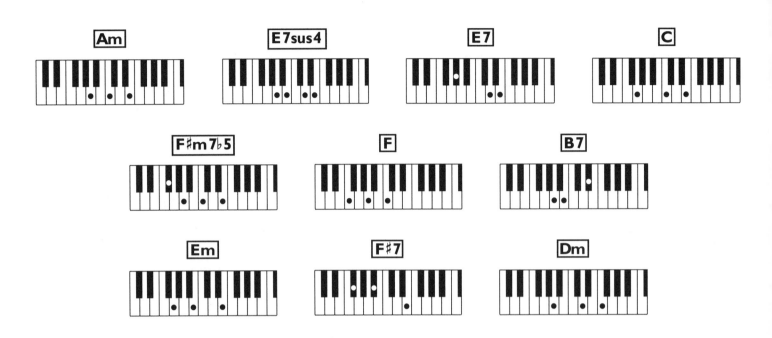

Voice: **Clarinet**

Rhythm: **Love Ballad**

Tempo: ♩. = 69

Ev-'ry-thing you are, ev-'ry-thing you'll be, touch-es the cur-rent of love so deep in

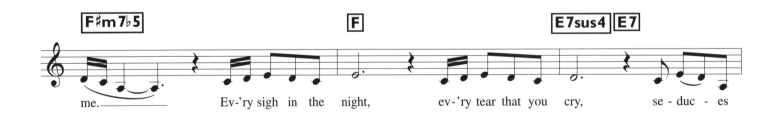

me.____ Ev-'ry sigh in the night, ev-'ry tear that you cry, se - duc - es

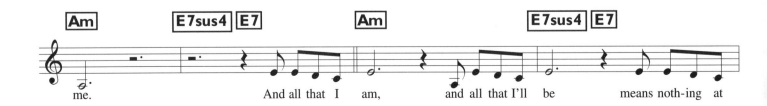

me. And all that I am, and all that I'll be means noth-ing at

TELL HIM

Words & Music by Linda Thompson, Walter Afanasieff & David Foster

© Copyright 1997 One Four Three Music, USA/Peermusic (UK) Limited, 8-14 Verulam Street, London WC1 (33.34%),
Wally World Music, USA/Sony/ATV Music Publishing (UK) Limited, 10 Great Marlborough Street, London W1 (33.33%) &
Brandon Brody Music, USA/Warner Chappell Music Limited, Griffin House, 161 Hammersmith Road, London W6 (33.33%).
All Rights Reserved. International Copyright Secured.

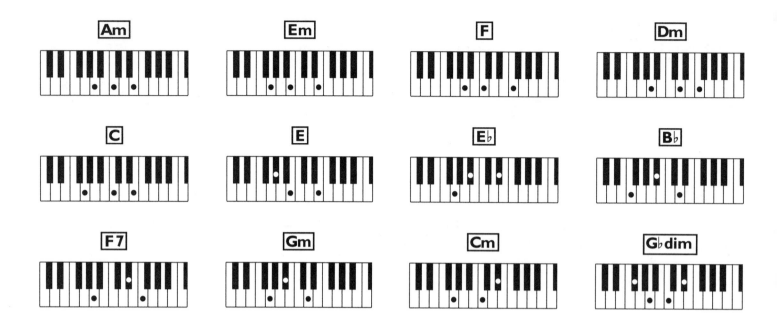

Voice: **Pan Flute**

Rhythm: **Pop Ballad**

Tempo: ♩ = 80

I'm scared, so a - fraid to show I care.

Will he think me weak if I trem - ble when I speak?

There's an - oth - er one he's think - ing of,

may - be he's in love, I'd feel like a fool, life can be so

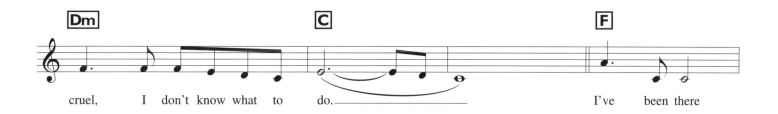

cruel, I don't know what to do.___ I've been there

with my heart out in my hand,___ but what you must un - der -

- stand, you can't let the chance to love him pass you by.___

Tell___ him, tell him that the sun and moon rise in his eyes, reach

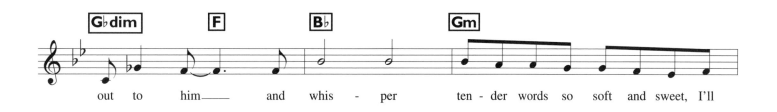

out to him___ and whis - per ten - der words so soft and sweet, I'll

hold him close to feel his heart-beat, love will be the gift you give you - self.___

THE COLOUR OF MY LOVE

Words & Music by David Foster & Arthur Janov

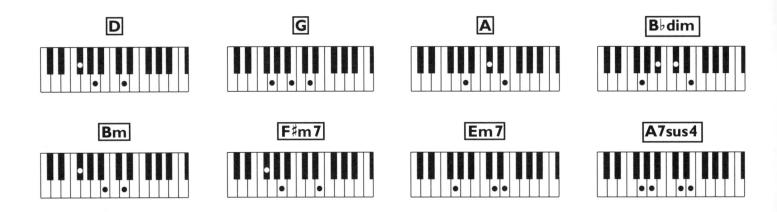

Voice: **Marimba**

Rhythm: **Epic Ballad**

Tempo: ♩ = 62

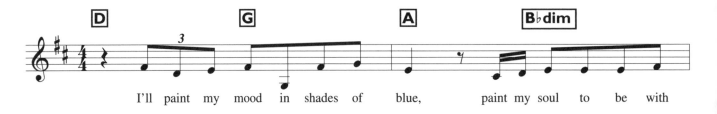

I'll paint my mood in shades of blue, paint my soul to be with

you. I'll sketch your lips in sha-ded tones, draw your mouth to my own.

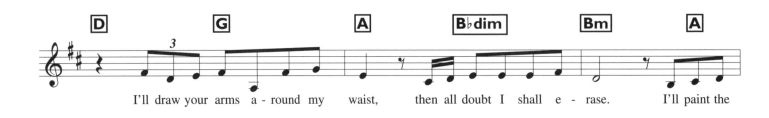

I'll draw your arms a-round my waist, then all doubt I shall e-rase. I'll paint the

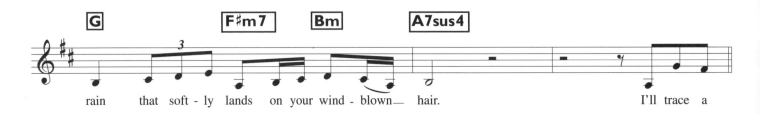

rain that soft-ly lands on your wind-blown— hair. I'll trace a

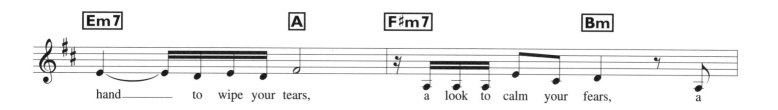

hand———— to wipe your tears, a look to calm your fears, a

sil - hou - ette———— of dark and light, while we hold each oth - er——— oh so———

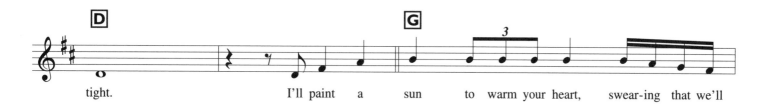

tight. I'll paint a sun to warm your heart, swear-ing that we'll

nev - er part, that's the col - our of my

love. I'll paint the truth, show how I feel, try to make you

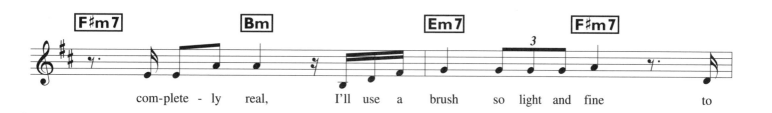

com-plete - ly real, I'll use a brush so light and fine to

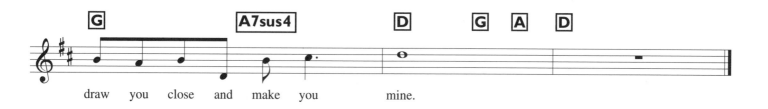

draw you close and make you mine.

THE LAST TO KNOW

Words & Music by Philip Galdston & Brock Walsh

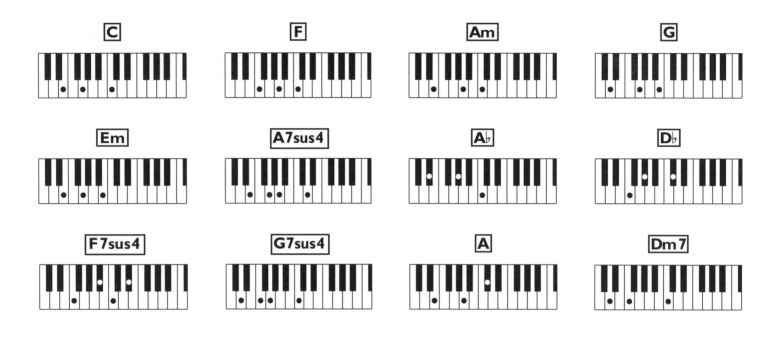

Voice: **Pop Ballad**

Rhythm: **Gut Guitar**

Tempo: ♩ = 75

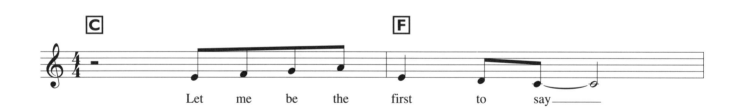

Let me be the first to say —

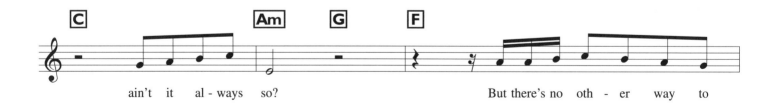

ain't it al-ways so? But there's no oth-er way to

find out what I need to know. It's not that I don't think you care, —

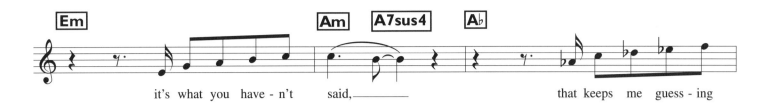

it's what you have-n't said,_____ that keeps me guess-ing

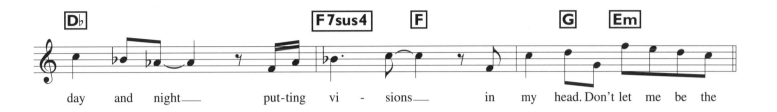

day and night___ put-ting vi - sions___ in my head. Don't let me be the

last, don't let me be the last, or would you

lie to me,___ don't___ you keep it to your-self for my pro-tec - tion, break it to me

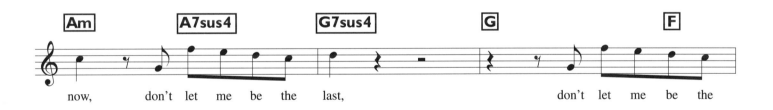

now, don't let me be the last, don't let me be the

last, or would you lie to me, ba-by all I ask___ don't

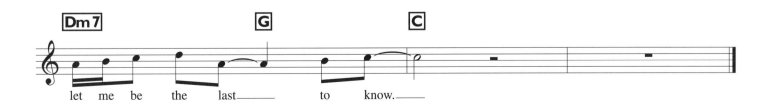

let me be the last___ to know.___

THE POWER OF LOVE

Words & Music by Candy de Rouge, Gunther Mende, Jennifer Rush & Susan Applegate

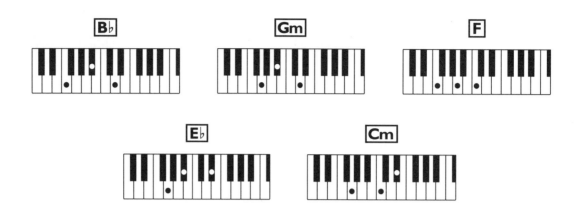

Voice: **Electric Piano 4**

Rhythm: **Soul Ballad**

Tempo: ♩ = 72

The whis - pers in the morn - ing _____ of lov - ers sleep - ing

tight, are roll - ing by like thun - der now

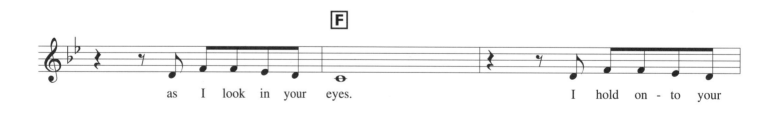

as I look in your eyes. I hold on - to your

bo - dy _____ and feel each move you make,

your voice is warm and ten-der,_____ a love that I could_____ not for-

-sake. 'Cause I'm your la - dy,_____

and you are my man,_____ when-ev-er you reach_

_____ for me, I'll do all that I can._____

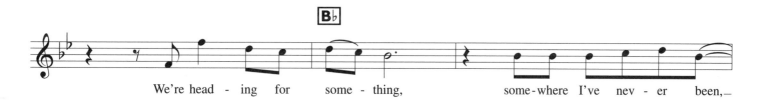

We're head-ing for some-thing, some-where I've nev-er been,_

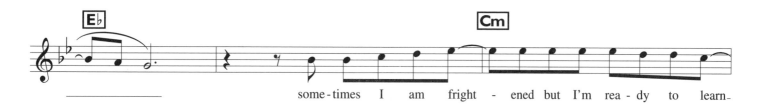

_____ some-times I am fright-ened but I'm rea-dy to learn_

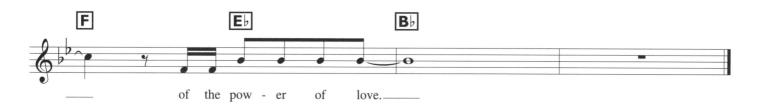

_____ of the pow-er of love._____

THINK TWICE

Words & Music by Andy Hill & Pete Sinfield

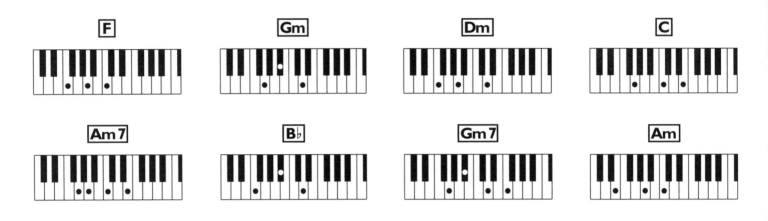

Voice: **Electric Guitar**

Rhythm: **Pop Rock 1**

Tempo: ♩ = 128

Don't think I can't feel that there's some - thing wrong.____

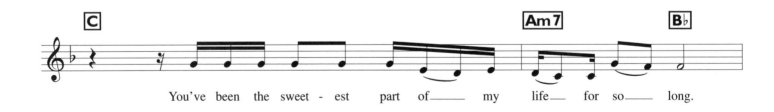

You've been the sweet - est part of____ my life____ for so____ long.

I look in your eyes there's a dis - tant light,____

and you and I know_____ there'll be a storm to - night._____

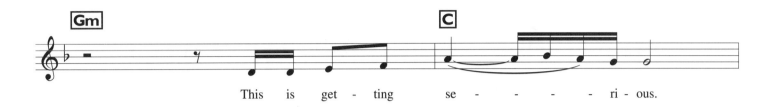

This is get - ting se - - - - ri - ous.

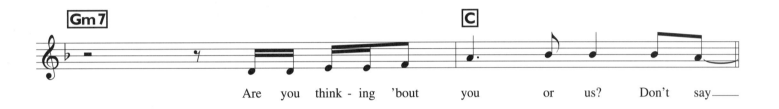

Are you think - ing 'bout you or us? Don't say_____

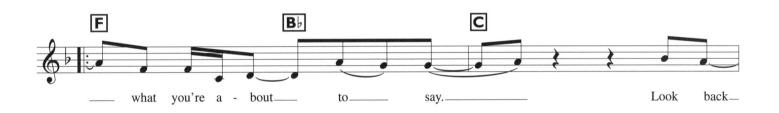

_____ what you're a - bout_____ to_____ say._____ Look back_____

_____ be - fore_____ you leave my_____ life. Be sure_____

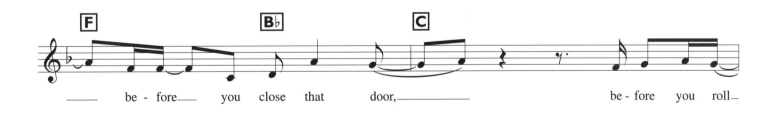

_____ be - fore_____ you close that door,_____ be - fore you roll_____

Repeat ad lib. to fade

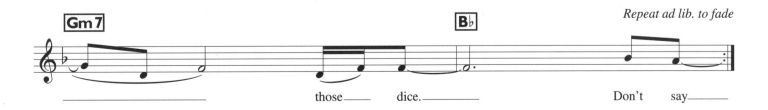

_____ those_____ dice._____ Don't say_____

WHEN I NEED YOU

Words & Music by Albert Hammond & Carole Bayer Sager
© Copyright 1977 Albert Hammond Enterprises Incorporated, Begonia Melodies
Incorporated & Stranger Music Incorporated, USA.
Windswept Pacific Music Limited, Hope House, 40 St. Peter's Road, London W6 (35%),
Warner Chappell Music Limited, Griffin House, 161 Hammersmith Road, London W6 (40%) &
Sony/ATV Music Publishing (UK) Limited, 10 Great Marlborough Street, London W1 (25%).
All Rights Reserved. International Copyright Secured.

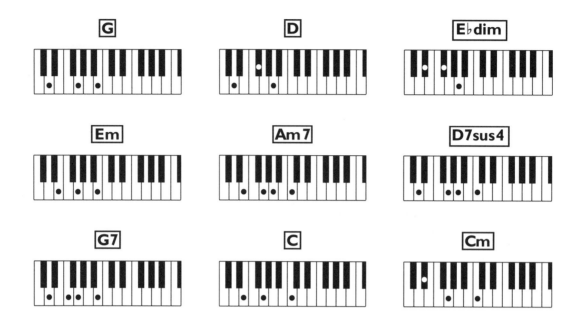

Voice: **Gut Guitar**

Rhythm: **Dance Pop 1**

Tempo: ♩ = 126

When I — need you, I just close my eyes and I'm

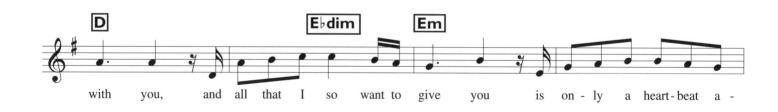

with you, and all that I so want to give you is on-ly a heart-beat a-

-way. — When I need love, I hold out my hands and I touch love, I

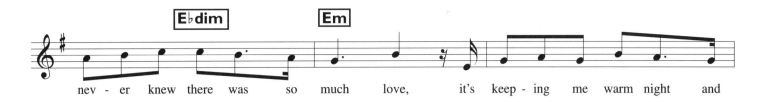

never knew there was so much love, it's keep-ing me warm night and

day. Miles and miles of emp-ty space in - be -

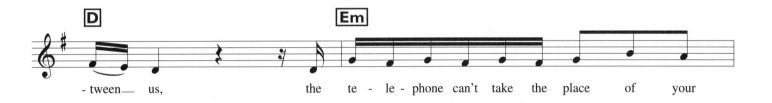

- tween us, the te - le - phone can't take the place of your

smile. But you know I won't be trav-el-ling for-ev-er, it's

cold out, but hold out and do like I do, oh I need you.

EASIEST KEYBOARD COLLECTION

Easy-to-play melody line arrangements for all keyboards with chord symbols and lyrics. Suggested registration, rhythm and tempo are included for each song together with keyboard diagrams showing left-hand chord voicings used.

 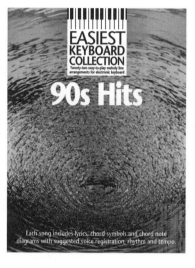 

Showstoppers

Consider Yourself (Oliver!), Do You Hear The People Sing? (Les Misérables), I Know Him So Well (Chess), Maria (West Side Story), Smoke Gets In Your Eyes (Roberta) and 17 more big stage hits.
Order No. AM944218

Pop Classics

A Whiter Shade Of Pale (Procol Harum), Bridge Over Troubled Water (Simon & Garfunkel), Crocodile Rock (Elton John) and nineteen more classic pop hits, including Hey Jude (The Beatles), Imagine (John Lennon), Massachusetts (The Bee Gees) and Stars (Simply Red).
Order No. AM944196

90s Hits

Over twenty of the greatest hits of the 1990s, including Always (Bon Jovi), Fields Of Gold (Sting), Have I Told You Lately (Rod Stewart), One Sweet Day (Mariah Carey), Say You'll Be There (Spice Girls), and Wonderwall (Oasis).
Order No. AM944229

TV Themes

Twenty-two great themes from popular TV series, including Casualty, EastEnders, Gladiators, Heartbeat, I'm Always Here (Baywatch), Red Dwarf and The Black Adder.
Order No. AM944207

Also available...

Ballads, Order No. AM952116
Boyzone, Order No. AM958331
Broadway, Order No. AM952127
Chart Hits, Order No. AM952083
Christmas, Order No. AM952105
Classic Blues, Order No. AM950697
Classical Themes, Order No. AM952094

Film Themes, Order No. AM952050
Hits of the 90s, Order No. AM955780
Jazz Classics, Order No. AM952061
Love Songs, Order No. AM950708
Pop Hits, Order No. AM952072
60s Hits, Order No. AM955768
80s Hits, Order No. AM955779